YOUR
CAPT
U.S. N

Captain Barnaby, who knew both Orville and Wilbur Wright personally, is recognized as one of aviation's pioneers. He designed, built and flew his first glider in 1909. In fact, he holds Soaring Certificate #1 from the National Aeronautic Association.

Now Captain Barnaby has written the definitive book about everything anyone needs to know to successfully design and fly a paper airplane. He shows you exactly how to build the planes. He "blueprints" six basic models (including the Barnaby aerobatics championship model shown on the front cover, which recently took first prize at the International Paper Airplane Competition). Clear illustrations make each step in construction easy to follow. He has even included many tips and rules for holding paper airplane competitions.

YOU COULDN'T FIND A MORE QUALIFIED INSTRUCTOR! All you have to do now is find some paper and scissors to learn . . .

## HOW TO MAKE & FLY PAPER AIRPLANES

# HOW TO MAKE & FLY
# PAPER AIRPLANES
## by Captain Ralph S. Barnaby
## U.S. Navy (Ret.)

Illustrations by the author

BANTAM BOOKS · TORONTO · NEW YORK · LONDON

The author wishes to acknowledge with thanks the efforts of Robert W. Neathery, Director of the Science Museum of The Franklin Institute, as well as those of Richard Harbeck of the U.S. Department of Health, Education and Welfare, whose persuasion led to the writing of this book, and of Mrs. Barbara Williams, without whose editorial guidance and encouragement it would never have been completed.

▶◀

RLI: $\dfrac{\text{VLM 8.0}}{\text{IL 7-12}}$

HOW TO MAKE & FLY PAPER AIRPLANES
*A Bantam Book / published by arrangement with
Four Winds Press, A Division of
Scholastic Magazines, Inc.*

PRINTING HISTORY
*Four Winds Press edition published 1968
Bantam edition published June 1970*
2nd printing
3rd printing
4th printing
5th printing
6th printing
7th printing

*Bantam Books are published by Bantam Books, Inc., a National
General company. Its trade-mark, consisting of the words "Bantam
Books" and the portrayal of a bantam, is registered in the United
States Patent Office and in other countries. Marca Registrada.
Bantam Books, Inc., 666 Fifth Avenue, New York, N.Y. 10019.*

PRINTED IN THE UNITED STATES OF AMERICA

*To my wife Marg—who while viewing
the whole affair with jaundiced eye, suffered
in relative silence through its borning—
this book is lovingly dedicated.*

# Contents

# Introduction

Everyone knows who the Wright brothers were. They were two young bicycle manufacturers from Dayton, Ohio, who in 1903 built and flew the first successful airplane. But not everyone understands why the Wrights succeeded where so many had failed.

Men had got off the ground before Wilbur and Orville Wright, it's true, but only for moments and never as masters of their craft. The Wrights believed these failures were due to "the inability of the operators to balance and steer their craft." If man was ever to fly, they decided, he would have to have complete control in the air.

So it was to the problem of control that the Wrights first devoted themselves. In their shop in Dayton they built and experimented with model airplanes. They also built a wind tunnel and measured the air forces of lift and drag on wing models of many forms. They developed a theory of flight control and worked out its principles.

Next, using what they had learned in these experiments, they designed and built man-carrying gliders. During the summers of 1900 and 1901 they test-flew these gliders and modified their design. Finally, in the fall of 1902 on the sand dunes at Kitty Hawk, North

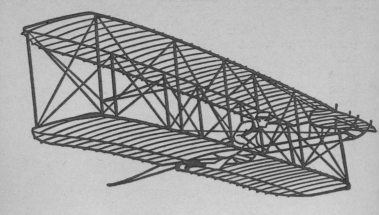

*Wilbur Wright in the 1902 glider.*

Carolina, the Wright brothers proved that their flight control system worked. They made more than two hundred manned gliding flights that fall—and broke all records for time and distance. Then, and only then, did they begin to design their first powered aircraft.

So one might say that the great contribution of the Wright brothers was not the flying machine at all, but the control system by which it flies. Without that system the Wrights would never have stayed off the ground for long periods of time or landed safely.

The principles of their system, devised in the bicycle shop at Dayton and flight-tested on the dunes at Kitty Hawk, have remained unchanged. In every aircraft today, from the smallest Piper Cub to the largest jetliner, it is the Wright brothers' control system that flies the craft. In the words of the patent office, the Wrights "reduced [flying] to practice."

The Wright brothers' approach is still good. In fact, I know of no better way for the beginner to learn the basics of flight and flight control than by experimenting, as they did, with model gliders. And the simplest models with which to start are those made of paper. We usually call them paper "airplanes," but really they are gliders, for they have no engines.

So in the pages that follow I will guide you along the flight path of the Wright brothers. You will learn to make and fly simple paper gliders and at the same time you will develop an understanding of the basic principles of flight and flight control.

Next, you will go on to build more sophisticated models. You will learn how to analyze their flying defects and how to make adjustments to correct and improve performance.

In the final chapters, you will find instructions for putting your models through aerial maneuvers and tips for holding paper airplane contests.

It is my hope that you will be encouraged to develop designs and construction methods of your own. Who knows, perhaps this hobby will lead you into a fascinating career in the aeronautical sciences? That's how I got started in aviation—by making model gliders.

Now, then, before you read on, get yourself a pad of 8 1/2-by-11-inch bond paper, some Scotch tape and paper clips, a stapler, and a ruler to help you bend and tear the paper neatly. If you want to be particularly neat, a pair of scissors will help. With these materials at hand, you are ready to make and fly paper airplanes.

# Simple Aerodynamics

Take a plain sheet of 8 1/2-by-11-inch paper. Drop it. Does it plunge to the ground like a rock? No. It slithers down, slipping from side to side, tumbling as it falls. The paper's descent is unpredictable. "Unstable" the engineers call it.

Fig. 1–1

Now take that same sheet of paper and tear or cut it from the middle of a long edge to the center of the sheet. Lap the cut edges to form a wide cone. Fasten the edges with a paper clip, a piece of Scotch tape, a staple or a dab of paste.

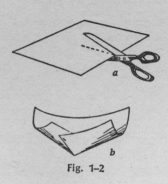

Fig. 1–2

Drop the cone.

See how the paper's pattern of action has changed?

Immediately the cone assumes a point-down attitude. It falls straight toward the floor, perhaps swaying gently from side to side.

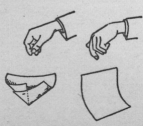

Fig. 1–3

With a simple change, you have made the cone stable. Regardless of how you drop it—on edge, upside down, right side up—the cone will always turn point down and descend that way.

## Air Resistance

Take another sheet of paper and the cone. Drop the two from the same height at the same time.

Which reached the floor first? The cone? It should have. The reason is that the cone meets less *air resistance*.

If you have ever tried to walk against a strong wind, you have experienced air resistance. The air is invisible, but you feel its presence because it is in motion. It has weight and substance and pushes against you. It resists your efforts to move it.

Fig. 1–4

Scientists have found that still air, too, resists the passage of an object through it. In fact, it doesn't matter whether the air, or the object or both are moving. There is still air resistance. In other words, resistance depends on the relative motion of the air and the object under consideration.

Other factors influencing air resistance are the size and shape of a moving object, its speed through the air and the density of the air. The greater the density, the greater the air resistance. That's easy to understand. Water, for example, is denser than air, and you know it's harder to push yourself through water than through air.

Changes in air density near the surface of the earth are caused by the weather, as indicated by changes in barometric (air) pressure. However these changes in air pressure—and, in turn, in air density—are so slight they will not affect the performance of paper airplanes. So for practical purposes you can think of the air density near the ground as unchanging.

Still another factor affecting air resistance is the amount of disturbance, or *turbulence,* that a moving object creates. Turbulence consists of little swirls and eddies in the air. If you could see turbulence in the air, it would look like water flowing around a rock (see Fig. 1–5).

Fig. 1–5

Experiments show that the greater the turbulence, the greater the air resistance. Because of its shape, the paper cone causes less turbulence than the tumbling sheet of paper. So the cone meets less air resistance and falls faster.

Roll your paper cone up tight until it looks like a pastry ice-cream cone. Now it falls faster, straighter

Fig. 1–6

and with less wobble. By streamlining its shape you have again reduced air resistance and increased *stability*, or steadiness in flight.

You can reduce air resistance still further by ballasting a sheet of paper so it will slice through the air edgewise. Take a fresh sheet and fold over a long edge five or six times. Paper-clip or staple the fold flat. This fold is now the forward, or *leading*, edge of your paper "wing."

Drop the wing, leading edge down. See how fast it falls? It has hardly disturbed the air at all.

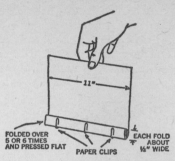

Fig. 1–7

You now have a paper model that slips through the air with little air resistance, or *drag*, as the engineers call it. But if you try to make it fly, the results will be disappointing. The paper quickly dives to the floor. It is unstable. It has no lift.

## What Is Lift?

*Lift* is the upward force that air exerts on an object aloft. It is the force that holds a craft in the air against the force of gravity. Lift comes about when the air pressure on the top surface of a wing is lower than the air pressure beneath it. So the wing is literally pushed upward by the greater air pressure.

Here's a demonstration of lift. Take a sheet of 8 1/2-by-11-inch paper and cut it in half widthwise. Then make a fold about 1 1/2 inches from a short edge (see dashed line in Fig. 1–8a). Fold the paper back and forth until it moves easily about the crease, like a hinge. Now, starting at the crease, pull the larger part of the paper over the edge of a table so that the paper takes on a curve, as shown in Fig. 1–8b.

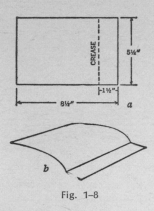

Fig. 1–8

Hold the edge of the flat narrow part against your lower lip. Now blow across the top of the flat surface. The curved part will rise high above the flat part, even though you are blowing right at it!

In blowing you have reduced the air pressure above the paper. The pressure beneath it being greater, the paper rises up.

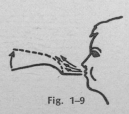

Fig. 1–9

But why, you may ask, is the pressure reduced when you seem to be blowing right at the paper? The reason is that you have increased the speed of airflow. According to what is known as Bernouilli's principle, the pressure of a fluid (liquid, or gas such as air) decreases as its speed increases, and vice versa.

Think of water flowing through a rubber hose. If you squeeze the hose, narrowing it at one place (see Fig. 1–10), the water will flow faster past the narrow section. Why? Because the same amount of water that traveled through the wide section in a given time must go past a narrow section in the same time. In fact, if the width of the passage is narrowed by half, the speed of flow is doubled and pressure is halved.

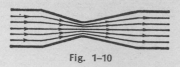

Fig. 1–10

An airplane wing, or *airfoil,* does the same kind of squeezing. But an airfoil provides only half the pinch. Still, the air flowing across the top of a wing is squeezed against the air above it (see Fig. 1–12). As a result, the air moves faster and pressure above the wing decreases. The air pressure beneath the wing is greater, so the wing is pushed up.

Early experimenters discovered that if the top surface of a wing has the right kind of curve and if the

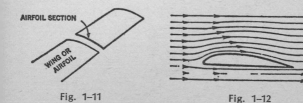

AIRFOIL SECTION

WING OR AIRFOIL

Fig. 1–11

Fig. 1–12

whole wing is tilted slightly in the direction of flight, the decrease of pressure on the top of the moving wing can be two or three times the size of the pressure from below.

Actually, when building paper planes, there is little need to worry about Bernouilli's principle and the increased lift of curved, or *cambered,* wings. Most paper models are so light in proportion to the surface area of their wings that lift is not a problem. In flying paper models, the chief problem is to keep drag low so that a model will slip through the air with the least turbulence. However, as you build heavier models, like some in Chapter 4, the additional lift gained by curving the wing surface will become important.

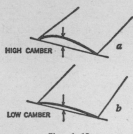

Fig. 1–13

Now that you understand how lift operates, let's see if you can give your paper wing a little lift and make it "flyable."

To produce maximum lift, the paper wing should be made to fly with its surface nearly horizontal. With the model in this position, the lift will act upward, counteracting the model's weight—the pull of gravity.

Take the wing weighted with paper clips. Hold the rear, or *trailing,* edge between thumb and index finger, thumb beneath the wing, index finger above it (see Fig. 1–14a). Scratch your index fingernail through the paper against the ball of your thumb. Scratch all along the

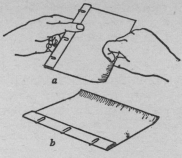

Fig. 1–14

trailing edge. That will curve up the edge and make it act as an elevator, balancing the weight at the leading edge. An *elevator* is an adjustable part of a horizontal surface that helps steer a model up and down.

Now you are ready for launch. Hold the wing gently between thumb and index finger, ahead of the trailing edge (see Fig. 1–15). Then launch it horizontally with a slight forward push.

Fig. 1–15

If you are lucky, your paper wing will fly after a fashion. If, instead, it dives into the ground, it is *nose heavy* and probably needs more up-elevator. Turn up the trailing edge more. If that doesn't work, remove a paper clip, too.

If, on the other hand, the wing does a series of dives and climbs like a roller coaster, it is *tail heavy*. It needs less up-elevator or perhaps more weight in front. Try adding another paper clip.

## Balance

You can see that balance is crucial in getting your model to fly properly. For perfect balance, a model should be adjusted so that its center of gravity in flight is at the same point as its center of lift.

The *center of gravity,* often called simply the CG, is a hypothetical point at which the mass of a model is concentrated. If a model were hung on a string from its center of gravity, it would balance in correct flying attitude.

The *center of lift,* or CL, is an imaginary point at which a model's total lift is concentrated. In fact, of course, a model's lift is distributed over its surface. But if the lift were concentrated at the center of lift, the effect on the model would be the same as that caused by the actual distribution of lift.

By folding up the leading edge of your paper wing and fastening it with paper clips, you moved the

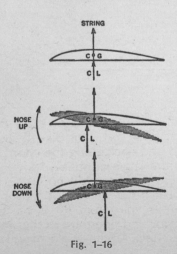

Fig. 1–16

model's center of gravity toward the nose. By turning up the trailing edge, you moved the center of lift forward, nearer the center of gravity.

Clearly the center of gravity is easily altered by increasing or decreasing the amount of weight at any point or by moving the fore-and-aft position of the weight, or both. The position of the center of lift is more complicated and depends on several factors: (1) the *planform,* or shape of the model as seen from directly above, (2) the *camber,* or wing curve, (3) the setting of the tail surfaces, (4) the model's airspeed, and (5) the angle of attack.

Since all these factors can be varied, it follows that flying characteristics and performance can in turn be varied, depending on how you set a model's surfaces and where you place its center of gravity.

*Angle of attack* is the angle between the chord of a wing and the direction of flight. It is the angle at which the wing strikes the air. The *chord* is the fore-and-aft dimension of a wing—the distance from leading to trailing edge.

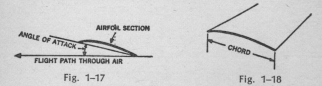

Fig. 1–17          Fig. 1–18

Wind tunnel experiments show that the center of lift on a rectangular test wing like that in Fig. 1–19 moves forward and back along the chord of the wing, depending on the angle of attack. Starting at the trailing edge, at zero angle there is no lift. As the angle of attack increases, the center of lift moves forward. At about 15 degrees, maximum lift is reached and the center of lift is located one-third of the way from leading to trailing edge. As the angle of attack is further

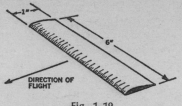

Fig. 1–19

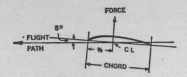

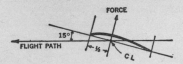

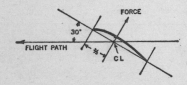

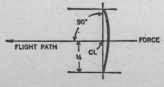

Fig. 1–20

increased, the center of lift starts moving back toward the midpoint of the chord.

Obviously, with lift moving back and forth, keeping a model balanced is a problem. Fortunately there are tricks to adjustment. You can set a model's surfaces in such a way that the very changes in angle of attack that displace the center of lift also produce counteracting forces that restore balance.

For example, you will recall that to make the simple paper wing fly normally it was necessary to bend up the trailing edge to give the model a little up-elevator. Let's consider what that adjustment did.

Suppose your paper wing, while gliding along, is hit by a gust or "bump" in the air. Its nose dips down, decreasing the angle of attack. Lift, too, immediately decreases, and the wing starts to dive. But in diving the wing speeds up. And in speeding up, downward pressure on the rear elevators is increased. This pressure, in turn, lifts the nose and restores normal gliding conditions (see Fig. 1–21).

So, in effect, by giving the model up-elevator you built into it the ability to right itself when it runs into "foul weather." You made it stable. And that is the topic of the next chapter.

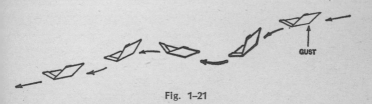

Fig. 1–21

# 2

# Stability and Control

The ability of a model to correct its flying attitude—its position in space—is called *stability*. To fly satisfactorily a paper airplane must be stable about the three axes of rotation: the roll (X–X), the pitch (Y–Y) and the yaw (Z–Z).

A paper airplane must not *roll*, or tip sideways about the X–X axis.

It must not *pitch*, or turn nose down or up about the Y–Y axis.

And it must not *yaw*, or turn right or left about the Z–Z axis.

In a man-operated aircraft, the pilot controls the movement of the craft about the roll, pitch and yaw axes by means of *control surfaces*—the ailerons, elevators and rudders, respectively. He changes the position of these surfaces as necessary to steer his craft.

A paper airplane has control surfaces, too, but they

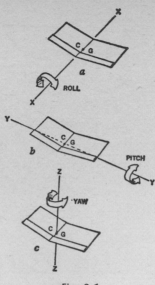

Fig. 2–1

are preset. They cannot be changed in flight. A model's surfaces must be adjusted before launch so that whatever happens to it in the air, it will automatically right itself and continue flying.

## Stability

You have already made your paper wing stable longitudinally (about the pitch axis) by weighting the nose and turning up the trailing edge. But the model will probably tend to roll from side to side.

You can make it stable laterally—that is, correct its tendency to roll—by giving the model *dihedral angle*. Simply fold the wing along its centerline so it becomes a model with *two wings,* whose tips are higher than the centerline (see Fig. 2–2).

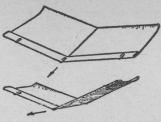

Fig. 2–2

Now if the model rolls sideways, as shown in Fig. 2–3, the low wing exposes more surface area to the vertical lift of the air than the high wing does. The greater upward force on the low wing raises it back up until the two wings are again even.

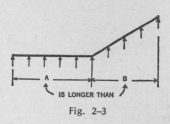

Fig. 2–3

Try flying the model now. It should coast downhill like a real glider.

Still, the model may tend to yaw, to veer off course. It is not directionally stable. To correct that fault, bend up a 1/2-inch strip along each wingtip. Your model now has rudders. A *rudder* is an adjustable vertical surface that steers a craft left or right. Bend the rudder to the left and the craft goes left; bend it to the right and the craft goes right.

Fly your model again. Does it persist in yawing? Look at it head on. To fly straight, the model must be perfectly symmetrical. The two sides should present

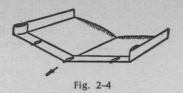

Fig. 2–4

exactly the same appearance. If one wing seems to have more angle of attack, as in Fig. 2–5a, twist or curl one trailing edge so the two wings match, as in Fig. 2–5b. Now test-fly the airplane. If it still yaws instead of gliding straight, bend the rear corners of the rudders right or left as necessary to correct the direction of flight (see Fig. 2–5c).

If it appears balanced but still yaws—say, to the left—try giving the left wing a slightly greater angle of

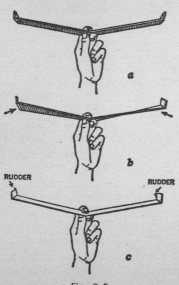

Fig. 2–5

attack, and therefore a little more lift, by curling its trailing edge down a bit. Or give the right wing less angle of attack and less lift (more up-elevator) by curling its trailing edge up. At the same time, apply a little right rudder. Now test-fly the model again.

## Roll and Rudder

The combined use of roll control (change in angle of attack of one wing with respect to the other) and rudder control was an innovation of the Wright brothers and an important feature of their control system.

The Wrights found that increasing the angle of attack of one wing not only increases its lift but also increases its drag. As a result, the craft turns toward the high side—a phenomenon known as "adverse yaw"—and then skids toward the low side. To counteract the added drag, they found it was necessary to apply opposite rudder.

But the lift-versus-drag effect is peculiar. It is seldom possible to predict which force will dominate. A model must be flown to find out. Often, if the change in wing angle is slight, the lift will prevail, and the model will turn toward the wing with the smaller angle of attack. Further increasing the angle of the same wing, however, may cause the increased drag to take charge, so that the model turns toward the side with the greater angle of attack.

The Wrights also learned that for an airplane to make a properly coordinated turn, or to straighten out from a turn, roll and yaw controls must be applied together and in the correct proportion.

If the *bank*, or tip-up, of the outer (higher) wing of a yawing craft is too great, the plane will *sideslip* toward the center of the turn. If the bank is insufficient, the aircraft will *skid* out away from the center of the turn.

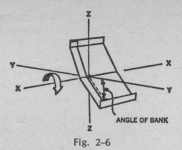

Fig. 2–6

To achieve and maintain just the right degree of bank and thus prevent skidding, the Wrights found, the angle of attack of one wing should be increased while the angle of the opposite wing is decreased. The Wrights did this by warping the wing structure of their gliders. Modern aircraft get the same effect by means of *ailerons*—hinged portions of the trailing edge out near the wingtips (see Fig. 2–7). On a paper airplane, you get aileron control by bending up or down the outer portions of the trailing edges of the wings.

Of course, in the flying wing model, and in darts and other tailless models, the trailing edges of the wings serve both as ailerons to roll the model to one side and as elevators to steer the model up and down. So they are called *elevons*.

When adjusting a model, it is best first to set the trailing edges as elevators to provide the proper longitudinal balance for steady flight. Then you can make

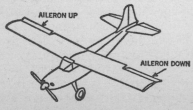

Fig. 2–7

roll corrections by increasing or decreasing the amount of up-elevator on one side or the other, as necessary.

## Ready for Launch

Let's review now what you have done. You started with a plain sheet of paper. First, you rolled up the leading edge and clipped it with additional ballast. Then you turned up the trailing edge, giving the model up-elevator. These two alterations provided pitch, or longitudinal, stability.

Second, you folded the model along the centerline, creating dihedral angle. This change provided roll, or lateral, stability. Finally, you turned the wingtips up into rudders, giving the model yaw, or directional, stability. In sum, with simple folds and distribution of weight you solved the problem of stability about the three axes of a craft.

The result is a paper flying machine in its simplest form. Of course, since it has no engine, the model is really a glider—not an airplane. To generate the lift that keeps it aloft your model must have enough forward speed. Some of this speed is imparted by your hand at launching. But it is mainly the pull of gravity that propels a model forward on its downhill path.

Think of coasting downhill on a sled or bicycle. A glider coasts downhill on the air. In fact, to keep flying it must keep coasting downhill. The only time a glider can go up is when it is coasting through air rising faster than the glider itself is sinking. Like a person walking down an "up" escalator moving up faster than he can walk down, the glider is carried upward by the rising air. We say it *soars*. Should your paper glider hit a hot air gust from a radiator, it might soar indoors.

To repeat, gravity supplies the power for the model's forward motion. But a glider does not simply fall. If that were the case, its path would be a simple tra-

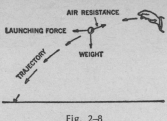

Fig. 2–8

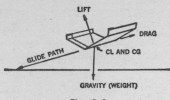

Fig. 2–9

jectory (Fig. 2–8). Rather, a glider follows a smooth course (Fig. 2–9) because of the lift of its wings.

The way you launch a glider is critical. Launched at the proper speed, a stable and well-adjusted model will glide steadily along a straight path, not diving or climbing, not turning right or left.

But what is "proper" launching speed? The only way to find it is trial and error, for it will vary with each new model, depending on planform, weight, wing area and general design. Only when launched at the correct gliding speed will a model follow a normal course.

Launched too fast, a stable model will climb until it slows down into a *stall*, then nose over and speed up again (Fig. 2–10). After a series of decreasing undulations, the model will end up in a smooth straight glide. We say the undulations have "damped out." Launched too slowly (Fig. 2–11), a stable glider will dive to pick

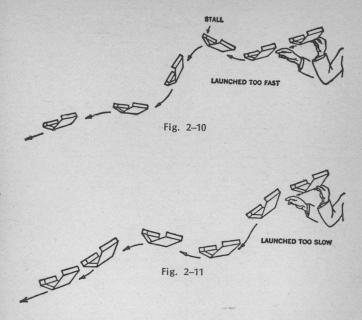

Fig. 2–10

Fig. 2–11

up speed, then end up in the same smooth glide. In both cases of bad launch, you lose distance and duration.

Now there is a secret to good launch. It's simply that a good launch isn't a launch at all. It's a *release*. Except for darts and javelin-type craft, you do not thrust a paper model into the air. You *just let it go*—with an almost imperceptible push, the very slightest forward motion.

## Review

By this time, you should be getting some "feel" for the forces at work on a paper model in the air (see Fig. 2–12). First, there is air resistance, or *drag*. The air has substance and resists displacement. Second, there is *gravity*, pulling the object toward the earth. Third,

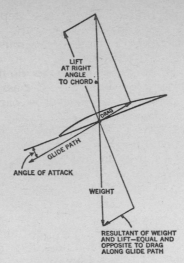

Fig. 2–12

there is *lift,* or buoyancy, the upward push of the sub-
stantial air against the object. And fourth, there is that
tiny initial forward motion imparted to the paper
model by your hand.

These forces operate simultaneously and interact in
complicated ways. For example, it is the ratio of lift to
drag that determines a model's *glide angle*—the slope
of the path down which a paper model will fly. So
that ratio also determines the distance a model will fly
when launched from a given altitude.

In altering the surfaces of your model to make it
stable you were, in fact, balancing the various effects
of the forces operating on it. This balancing act is
something you will have to go through many times.
Even when you become expert at folding paper, you
will still have to work on a model till its surfaces are
set just right and its center of gravity is at the proper
point. So before building the more advanced models

in Chapters 3 and 4, let's review the steps you must take to make a stable, straight-flying craft.

To fly satisfactorily, a paper plane must be stable from nose to tail. Your first step is to concentrate weight at the front of your model. You do that by folding or rolling the paper so most of its mass is up front. Or you can add weight at the nose—paper clips or staples. Or you can do both.

The effect of all the weight up front is to force the nose down when the glider is released in flight. To balance the weight up front, you must add up-elevator at the rear, or the paper airplane will plummet to the ground. So you curl up the trailing edge. This moves the center of lift forward to hold up the weighted nose in flight.

Here's what happens. At first, air pushes down against the trailing edge, counteracting the pull of gravity at the nose. So the model noses up and climbs. Now climbing with a glider is like going uphill on a sled. As it climbs, the glider slows down. And as it slows down, the downward push of air at the rear decreases. So then the nose drops, the flight path steepens and the glider speeds up in a downhill run—until once again the downward push of air on the elevators takes charge and lifts the nose. You see this process as the undulations described earlier.

The second important task in making a paper airplane is to achieve lateral and directional stability. In practice, this means getting your model to glide in a straight line.

As you construct each of the paper model airplanes described in the following pages, study it carefully along the centerline. Each model must be perfectly symmetrical, its two sides identical. Both wings must show exactly the same angle to the direction of flight. If one wing has more angle of attack than the other, the model will roll to one side. As it rolls, it will start to turn to that side—the side of the low wing.

If the model has fins or rudders, see that they, too, are set at the same angle to the centerline. If the rudders or the rear edges of the vertical fins are turned to one side, not only will the model itself turn, but the inside wing will drop. This tipping while turning with the inner wingtip lower than the outer wingtip is called *banking*.

In folding the paper, take care, too, that no twist develops, or you'll get results that look like sketch 2–5*b*, instead of sketch 2–5*a*. Remember that it takes only a slight difference in angle of surface to produce great changes in flight path. After each adjustment, test-fly your model and note the result.

**3**

# Darts and Flying Wings

Now that you understand the basic principles of gliding flight, you are ready to build more advanced kinds of paper model airplanes.

## A Simple Dart

Probably the most familiar paper model is the dart. I doubt that there is anyone who hasn't at one time or another folded a sheet of paper into a dart and launched it across a room or down a hall or out a window.

In case you have forgotten, here's how to make a simple dart. Fold a sheet of paper in half lengthwise, following drawing a in Fig. 3–1. Flatten it out again and lay it on a table with the crease up. Now fold over the two corners so they meet at the centerline (b). Then fold in the two sides so they, too, meet at the center-

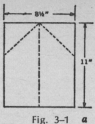

Fig. 3–1  *a*

line (*c*). Now fold the whole thing together along the centerline (*d*).

Next, make a keel. Starting at the nose, fold one side back at an angle to the centerline (*e*). Then turn the model over and fold the other side back so it exactly matches the first side. Now open these sides out at right angles to the center part, which becomes the keel (*f*). Fasten the folds of the keel together with a paper clip or a staple about three or four inches back from the nose. For safety's sake, it's smart to snip off the first inch of the dart's nose. Light as a dart is, its sharp point can inflict injury.

The finished dart should look like the one in Fig. 3–1*f*. Note that the model is bottomside up.

To launch the dart, grasp the keel between thumb and index finger, and give a good forward push. The dart should fly more like an arrow than a glider, making little use of the wing surfaces to stay aloft. Instead, it will follow a *trajectory*, a path determined by the force (thrust) and direction you give it at launch and by the downward pull of gravity. Like the feathers on the tail of an arrow, the dart's surfaces serve only to keep it going nose-first along its path.

The dart can be made to fly like an airplane, however, by giving it some up-elevator. So bend up the rear corners of its long triangular wings (see Fig. 3–1*h*). Now see how it flies. Instead of diving into the ground,

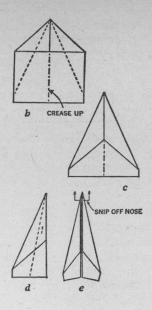

*b* CREASE UP

*c*

*d*     *e* SNIP OFF NOSE

*f*

*g*

*h*

Fig. 3–1

it should glide along, nose tilted up above the flight path, wings at a slight positive angle of attack to provide the lift necessary for support.

Notice that while the wings are flat from side to side —that is, without dihedral—the dart is quite stable laterally. It may tend to rock from side to side a bit, but it doesn't roll over. Obviously, there is another way to achieve lateral stability. The secret is the keel projecting below the wings. If the dart starts to roll sideways, air spills out from under the high wing. At the same time, the keel entraps air under the low wing (see Fig. 3–2). This air beneath the low wing exerts enough force to raise it until both wings are level again.

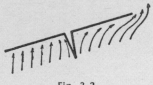

Fig. 3–2

## More Darts

Some readers may have made darts somewhat differently—by laying the sheet with the centerline crease down instead of up and then folding in the corners to meet at the centerline (see Fig. 3–3).

The rest of the procedure is the same. You fold the sides in to the centerline, then fold the whole model together and open the wings outward. Notice that with this method, the folded-up edges are inside the keel and on top of the wing rather than outside the keel and under the wing as in the dart in Fig. 3–1. You should secure the keel with a paper clip or staple, as before. And again, it's wise to snip the nose.

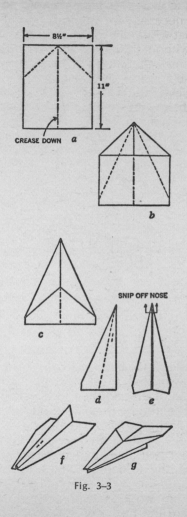

Fig. 3–3

This dart flies just as nicely as the first model. The same adjustments for good gliding flight apply.

Another variation on the basic dart model can be had by making the final outward fold of the wings closer to the centerline than the folds in Fig. 3–1c. The result is a model with more *wingspan* (distance from wingtip to wingtip) and more wing area but less keel. It's a good idea to give this model a little dihedral to restore the lateral stability lost by reducing the depth of the keel (see Fig. 3–4).

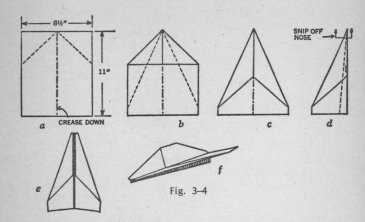

Fig. 3–4

The simple, slender dart is probably the fastest of the gliders, but it is not very maneuverable. Its long keel and long wing surfaces make it "tender" laterally. It is possible to adjust a simple dart to fly a gentle turning path by using the rear end of the keel as a rudder. But if too much rudder is applied, the model will tend to roll over and dive into the ground because of its narrow wingspan.

A more flyable dart is the modified version in Fig. 3–5. Fold a sheet of paper in half widthwise. Spread the paper out crease up (a), and fold over the cor-

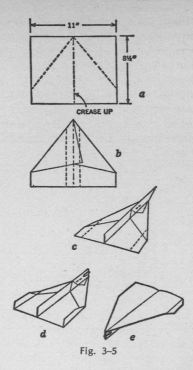

Fig. 3–5

ners so they lap at the centerline (*b*). Now fold the sheet together again along the centerline and fold the sides back. Make the folds about one inch from the centerline fold and parallel to it (*c*). Staple the keel, snip off the pointed nose and add a paper clip. Now turn up the wingtips (*d*).

Up to this time the model has been on its back. Now turn it right side up and give it some up-elevator (*e*). If you wish, instead of curling the trailing edges, you may try the elevons shown in Fig. 3–6 for lateral and pitch control.

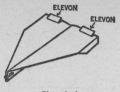

Fig. 3–6

With a little elevator adjustment and shifting of the paper-clip ballast on the keel, this dart should fly pretty well. By bending the rear edges of the turned-down wingtip fins, you can make the model glide in a straight or a curved path. However, because of its long keel, this dart will still not be very maneuverable.

## Dart Into Wing

Another step in getting away from the dart planform is to increase the span-to-length ratio, as shown in the model in Fig. 3–7. Here, as before, you fold the center-line across the short dimension of the sheet. Lay the paper out flat with the crease up and fold in the corners to meet at the centerline (b). Next, fold the pointed nose back to the spot where the folded corners meet (c). Fold the leading edge back about half-way to that spot (d).

Now fold the sheet together, and open back the wings to make a keel about three-fourths of an inch deep. Fold up a 1/2-inch strip along each wingtip. Then put two paper clips on the nose and give the model a bit of up-elevator, either by curling up the trailing edges or cutting elevons. For good roll stability, give this model a little dihedral.

Have you noticed that the model looks a lot like the first one you built, the flying wing in Fig. 2–4? Let's make another wing similar to that first one and see what you can do to make it more maneuverable and a little less tender.

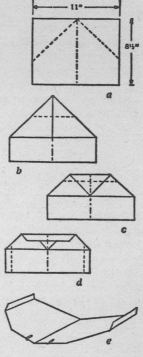

Fig. 3–7

## A Flying Wing

Take an 8 1/2-by-11-inch sheet and fold it in half widthwise. Lay it down on a flat surface with the crease up and then fold it in half again, this time lengthwise (see Fig. 3–8a).

Next, fold over a 1/4-inch strip along one 11-inch edge. Continue folding over this edge until you reach the lengthwise center crease. Be sure that the folds are parallel to the trailing edge. In other words, be sure the distance from the leading edge of the fold to the trailing edge of the wing is everywhere 4 1/4 inches. The crease will serve as a guide.

Now spread out your hands and press the folded roll flat (b). Fasten the roll in place with a strip of Scotch tape, as shown (c). Turn the model over so the taped roll faces down and curl up the trailing edge ever so slightly (d). Test-fly the model. Like the first flying wing, this model should glide after a fashion.

You might try making the rectangular flying wing out of light vellum tracing paper instead of the heavier bond paper you have been using. When properly balanced and carefully adjusted, this lightweight wing has the flattest gliding angle and the lowest *sinking speed* (rate of loss of altitude) of any model I know. For directional and roll stability, a slight dihedral angle is advisable. Despite its simple appearance, the vellum wing is tricky to adjust.

If you give either the vellum or bond wing some dihedral and turn up its wingtips (e), you'll get a much more stable performance. This improved model resembles a successful man-carrying soaring plane, the Flying Plank shown in Fig. 3–9.

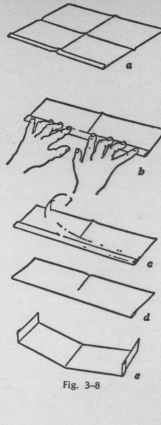

Fig. 3–8

Fig. 3–9

## A Modified Flying Wing

Here's something else you can try with the flying wing model. Fold the wingtips together, as shown in Fig. 3–10a, and then at about the midpoint of the wing chord make a 1 1/2-inch cut in toward the centerline fold. Flatten out the model. Turn up a 1/2-inch strip along the wingtip forward of the cut, then turn *down* all of the cut portion along the rear of each wingtip.

Now curl up the trailing edge slightly to give up-elevator. After checking to see that the model is symmetrical when viewed from dead ahead, launch it as shown in Fig. 1–15. You will find that this model performs pretty well. Not only will it make good straight glides, but if launched in a banked attitude (see instructions on page 61), it will fly a circle.

This last model leads us right to the author's own prize-winning design, the Barnaby Aerobatics Champion, which you will learn to build in the next chapter.

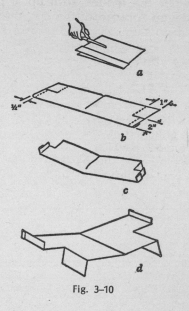

Fig. 3–10

# 4

# The Barnaby and
# Other Models

I had the good fortune to grow up during the years
that the Wright brothers were building and flying their
aircraft. During the summer of 1908, the Wrights were
making their first public flights—Wilbur in Europe and
Orville in the United States. I was spending the vaca-
tion working in my father's engineering office in New
York City. I followed eagerly the reports of the Wrights'
exploits and resolved then that aviation would be my
field. I started folding up and flying paper airplanes,
using office stationery. That explains my preference
for 8 1/2-by-11-inch bond.

The model I developed then has remained substan-
tially unchanged over the years. It resembles more
than most models I know the popular light airplanes
like the Piper Cub, the Aeronca and the Cessna. Like

them, the Barnaby is a versatile flier. With slight adjustments, it is capable of performing straight glides, right and left circles that return to the hand of the launcher, and perfect loops.

For a really neat job you'll need a pair of scissors to cut the paper to its final planform. But it is quite possible to tear the paper to shape by hand and get acceptable results. In fact, I acquired my tearing skill while making free balloon flights from Wright Field, near Dayton, in the late 1920's. I would while away the time by tearing out, folding up and dropping paper gliders from the balloon—then watch them circle below until lost from sight.

## How To Build
## A Barnaby Model

Here's how to make a Barnaby model. Take a sheet of 8 1/2-by-11-inch bond paper and fold it in half widthwise (Fig. 4–1a). Open it and lay it crease down on a hard flat surface. This crease will be the model's centerline.

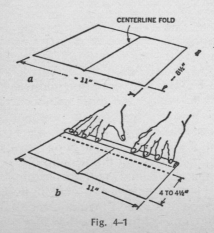

Fig. 4–1

Fold over a 1/4-inch strip along one of the 11-inch edges. Do this in one operation, using the fingers of both hands. The fold must lie flat. Continue folding until at least one-half of the sheet has been folded up (b). Remember, each fold must be carefully flattened in a separate operation. Otherwise, you may build a twist into the leading edge. Later, when you try to adjust the model, the wings will not align.

Now bring the two rolled-up tips together and press again along the centerline. Hold the paper in this position and carefully cut or tear along the dotted line, as indicated in Fig. 4–1c. Spread the model out flat and turn up a quarter inch of each wingtip to make wing fins. These fins should be parallel to the centerline and perpendicular to the wings (d).

Next, fold *down* the outer portions of the tail surfaces to make rudders, following the angle made by the dashed lines in Fig. 4–1e. Note that these folds are not parallel to the centerline but toe in slightly toward the nose.

With thumb and index finger, bend up a small portion of the rolled-up leading edge at the centerline (f). This raised portion will act as a truss to stiffen the wings laterally and hold them at the proper angle.

Now camber the wings by scratching along their trailing edge (g), as you learned earlier. Hold the model by the tail, between the thumb and first two fingers with the index finger on top and check for symmetry (h). If necessary, add more camber to one wing or smooth one out until the two are identical.

Also, check for wingtip symmetry by viewing the model from the side. If the leading edge has been folded right, the creases of the wingtip fins will appear parallel to the centerline (i). If the leading edge has not been folded right, these fins may be twisted down (j), or one may be twisted down and the other up (k). It's practically impossible to get rid of such a fault once

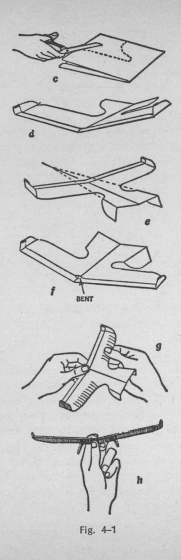

Fig. 4–1

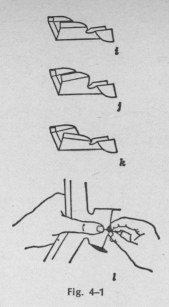

Fig. 4–1

it has been folded into the model. It's easier to start over again with a fresh sheet of paper.

Finally, give the model a little up-elevator by pinching a bit of the center fold at the tail (*l*).

You are now ready for launch. Hold the model as shown in Fig. 4–2 and push it gently away from you on a slightly downward path. If you have correctly executed each step in construction, your model should glide along nicely. If not, adjustments must be made.

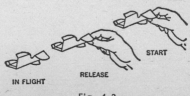

IN FLIGHT    RELEASE    START

Fig. 4–2

## How To Make Adjustments

If the model dives into the ground, give it a little more up-elevator by cambering the trailing edge of the tail upward.

If the model follows an undulating path, it has too much up-elevator. Try flattening down the trailing edge of the tail. If this doesn't work, chances are your Barnaby is tail-heavy because you did not roll up enough paper in the leading edge. This can be corrected by adding a paper clip to the nose.

If the model glides all right but tends to yaw, check again for symmetry. Make sure both wings have the same amount of camber. And make sure, too, that both rudders have the same amount of toe-in. If the airplane still tends to yaw, increase the camber on the side to which it turns. Then bend the trailing edge of the rudders toward the other side. Remember to keep your corrections small.

Perhaps you are wondering why I told you to toe in the rudders instead of making them parallel to the centerline. The aerodynamic explanation is quite complex, but the simple fact of the matter is the model flies better that way.

You may have noticed that most professional weather vanes are made with split surfaces at the rear (Fig. 4–3). It has been found that they make the arrow point more steadily into the wind with less wavering of the vane from side to side. The same is true of the toed-in rudders. They keep the glider on course and they keep it steady.

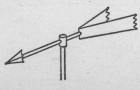

Fig. 4–3

## Cardboard Construction

So far we have limited ourselves to paper models folded up from sheets of paper. In most cases, the folded-up portion serves two purposes, first to furnish the necessary ballast at the front of the model, and second, to give the necessary stiffness to the leading edge of the wing. It does, however, restrict somewhat the model's planform.

You can get around that obstacle if instead of folding up the leading edge, you use a cardboard strip with a suitable adhesive for ballast and stiffening. I find that the weight of cardboard slipped in freshly laundered shirts is excellent for the purpose. This cardboard leading edge may be applied to either the top or bottom surface, depending on the model's design. In models with centerline keels, of course, the cardboard would have to go on the top.

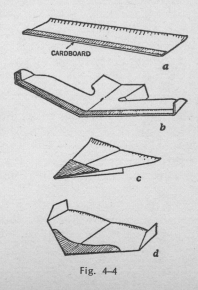

Fig. 4–4

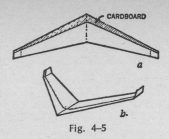

Fig. 4–5

Instead of glue or paste-type adhesive, I recommend using rubber cement to apply the cardboard. Ordinary pastes and glues often contain water, which tends to soften and distort the paper. Rubber cement will not do this.

Figure 4–4 shows several models similar to ones you made earlier—but using cardboard leading edges and nose sections instead of folded-up leading edges.

Of course, it may be necessary to try various widths of cardboard to attain the desired balance. If the ballast is insufficient, one or more paper clips or another strip of cardboard may be necessary.

Cardboard construction opens up a whole new field of paper models, particularly in the flying wing category. Figures 4–5, 4–6 and 4–7 show three typical planforms, their folding diagrams and the finished craft. Shaded areas indicate the cardboard ballast. Note that two of the models have keels.

Figure 4–8 shows a head-on view of the last model. The wings are twisted at the tips to lend stability to the craft.

Incidentally, a paper and cardboard copy of the mapleseed, nature's rotary wing aircraft and forerunner of the autogiro, can be made as shown in Fig. 4–9.

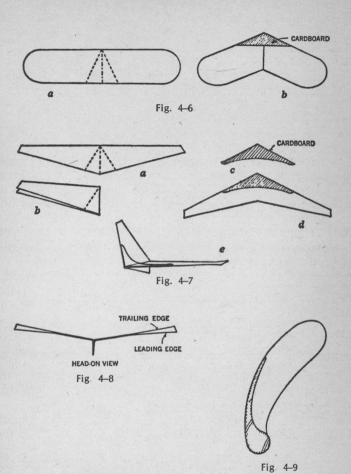

Fig. 4–6

Fig. 4–7

Fig 4–8

Fig 4–9

## Canards

Another planform that lends itself to cardboard ballast is the canard, or tail-first glider. "Canard" is the French word for wild duck. That bird's head is set on a long neck way in front of its body. Similarly, the horizontal stabilizer and control surfaces of canard aircraft are located out in front of the main wing.

Fig. 4–10

All the early gliders flown by the Wright Brothers were canards (see illustration on page x), as were their first powered machines. Today, one proposed version of the new supersonic transport is a tail-first design.

Canards can take many forms. You can convert the darts in Figs. 3–1 and 3–4 to canards by fastening a small triangular surface to the nose. Use rubber cement or a staple, as shown in Fig. 4–11.

For proper longitudinal stability, canards require some modification. First, the little front wing must be given a greater angle of attack than the main wing. Curl down the front wing's trailing edge to give it a slight upward tilt. Second, the extra lift generated by the little front wing moves the glider's center of lift forward. So you should ballast the model at the nose for proper balance. Use a small triangle of cardboard or add a clip.

In addition to these typical paper airplane designs, it is possible to duplicate the planforms of some of

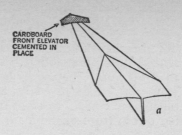

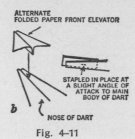

Fig. 4–11

nature's soaring experts, such as the sea gull and the albatross (Fig. 4–12). Others, like the turkey buzzard, the eagle and the condor (Fig. 4–13), while superb soarers, are less easy to represent in practical flying paper forms, for it is difficult to keep the fingerlike wingtip feathers in proper alignment.

In Fig. 4–14 the albatross model is in flight. You will notice it was necessary to cheat a bit on the tail. Instead of imitating nature, I made a toed-in tail like the one on the Barnaby model. In flight a bird can spread, contract and twist its tail feathers to get control. But a model can't. The toe-in makes up for the difference.

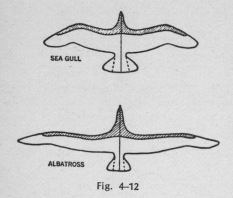

Fig. 4–12

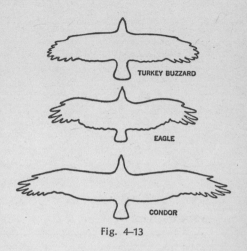

Fig. 4–13

Fig. 4–14

# 5

# Paper Airmanship

I am sure that by now you will have discovered there is a lot more to making and flying paper airplanes than just folding up sheets of paper and tossing them into the air. From first fold to launch, your skill and know-how determine the performance of a model. At the most elementary level, they make the difference between a model that falls and one that flies. At a more advanced stage, they give extra distance and time in flight, and enable you to put your model through aerial maneuvers such as circles, turns and loops.

In previous chapters you learned the basics of making and flying paper airplanes: how to achieve stability by proper location of the center of gravity and center of lift, how to adjust surfaces, and how to launch a model in a normal straight glide.

In this chapter I would like to talk about the fine points of making and flying paper airplanes: folding and cutting the paper, locating control surfaces, setting control surfaces, and launching the model in aerial maneuvers.

## Folding and Cutting

It's hard to believe there can be right and wrong ways of folding a piece of paper, but there are. Take, for instance, the usual first step in making most models: "Fold the sheet in half (either lengthwise or widthwise, depending on the design) to establish the model's centerline."

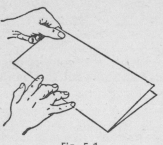

Fig. 5–1

That direction sounds simple enough. But you must remember that this is a most important fold for it establishes the basic fore-and-aft symmetry about which the model is shaped. The center fold, therefore, must be straight and divide the sheet exactly in half.

I have found this method of folding best. First bend the sheet over, placing the corners together. Then, holding the edges firmly in place with one hand, flatten down the sheet with the other hand to make a sharp, straight crease. Don't start at one end and run a finger along to form the crease. Spread out your free hand and press down the whole fold at once. That way you will not put a twist in the sheet.

Avoiding twists in the wings of models with folded-up leading edges (like the flying wing and Barnaby models) is not too easy. After many years of folding up the leading edges of my Barnaby models in the manner described on page 42, I have hit upon what I believe may be an even better technique. I worked it out while writing this book.

After making the centerline crease, spread the sheet out flat again and fold it in half once more—this time lengthwise—to establish another centerline crease at right angles to the first. The purpose of the fold is to show you how far to roll up the leading edge.

The next step is to spread the sheet out flat again and fold over a 1/4-inch strip along the longer (11-inch) edge. *Roll* this folded strip over and over until you have reached the lateral crease—that is, until half the sheet has been rolled up. Now, spreading out your fingers, flatten down the roll in one operation, as shown in Fig. 5–2. Then cut the model to shape, as shown in Fig. 5–3.

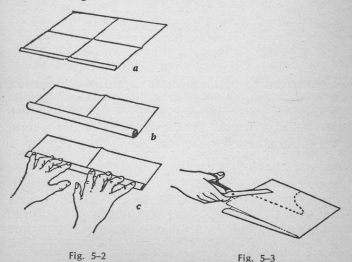

Fig. 5–2                    Fig. 5–3

To assure symmetry in the planforms of Barnaby models and other specially shaped designs—that is, to make sure the right and left sides are exactly the same —do the cutting or tearing while the two halves of the sheet are folded together.

## Locating Control Surfaces

For the greatest effectiveness, control surfaces should be located as far as possible from a model's center of gravity. The forces generated by those surfaces are thus able to exert the greatest leverage upon the axis of rotation they control. In practice, this means that the elevators, which control pitching about the Y–Y axis, should be as far to the rear as possible—or, in the case of a canard, as far to the front as possible. The ailerons, which control roll about the X–X axis, should be out near the wingtips. The rudders, which control yaw about the Z–Z axis, should be as far rearward as design permits.

Another point is that for directional stability the major part of vertical control surfaces such as keels, fins and rudders must be behind the center of gravity. In that position they work like the feathers on the tail of an arrow to keep the model flying nose first.

So in the case of swept-wing or V-type models, like that in Fig. 5–4, all the control surfaces must be at the wingtips. If the V-model also has a center keel, like the dart in Fig. 5–5, you can simply use the trailing edges of the wingtips as elevons. No rudders are

Fig. 5–4

Fig. 5–5

needed. For a turn, just increase up-elevon on the side toward which the turn is desired.

If a V-model has no center keel, wingtip fins are advisable. Note, though, that because of the sweep-back of the wings, such a model—even without keel or fins—can be made to fly satisfactorily with less diffi-culty than a rectangular flying wing.

## Setting of Control Surfaces

In man-carrying airplanes and gliders, the pilot op-erates the control surfaces to make the aircraft climb or descend and to make it perform properly banked turns and other flight maneuvers. In paper models, however, the controls are usually set for a straight-line glide. Once so set, the only change thereafter for most maneuvers will be in the amount of up-elevator.

For instance, if you want a model to fly a horizontal circle, the amount of up-elevator you apply will de-termine the diameter of the circle. The smaller the diameter desired, the greater the up-elevator needed. In most cases, circular flight will take some increase in up-elevator over that used for the normal straight glide. So will looping flight. But no change in ailerons and rudders is necessary. They should remain set for straight flight.

## Launching a Model in Aerial Maneuvers

The kinds of maneuvers that can be made with paper airplanes depend on (1) adjustments of control surfaces before launch, since there is no way of chang-ing them in flight, and (2) technique of launching. Technique of launching in turn breaks down into speed of launching, attitude of model at time of re-lease and direction of release.

The maneuvers most easily performed with paper airplanes are circles, turns and loops. But before a model can execute any maneuver it must be made to fly a straight-line glide. This is critical. If a model does not fly a straight glide, it will not perform maneuvers properly. So let's review the straight glide launching.

If the model has a keel, grasp it by the keel between thumb and index finger. If the model has no keel, hold it by the body ahead of the trailing edge. Make sure the wings are level and aim the nose along what you believe to be the normal glide path. Move the model ahead along the projected flight path at what you estimate to be the gliding speed. Release the model.

Take care that you do not alter the attitude of the model as you launch it. Keep your eye on the model and concentrate on the centerline. Think of moving your hand in a path parallel to the centerline.

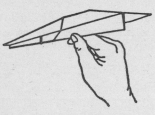

Fig. 5–6

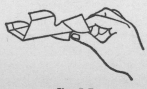

Fig 5–7

Also, don't release the model with a snap of the wrist. You will change the model's flight path. Instead, follow through with your launching arm.

Remember, practice makes perfect!

Once you have the straight glide launching down pat, you are ready for maneuvers.

## Circles

Circular flights are made in a path more or less parallel to the ground. Most paper airplanes, except the darts, can fly circles, but the best performers are the models with greater wing span like the Barnaby and the swept-wings.

Whether a model flies a full or partial circle depends on (1) the amount of up-elevator applied, (2) the angle of bank at which the model is released and (3) the speed of launching.

Here are directions for launching models in right and left turns. I assume you are right-handed. If you are left-handed, simply alter the instructions as necessary.

Grasp keel-bearing models between thumb and index finger. Grasp keel-less models by the nose. Hold the model in a vertical bank, underside toward you.

Now, for a circle to the left, hold the model at your left, nose pointing toward the right (Fig. 5–8). Quickly and smoothly draw your hand straight across to the

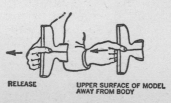

RELEASE          UPPER SURFACE OF MODEL
                 AWAY FROM BODY

Fig 5–8

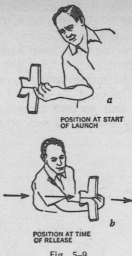

POSITION AT START
OF LAUNCH

POSITION AT TIME
OF RELEASE

Fig. 5–9

right. Release the airplane without changing this line. Any twist of the wrist will cause erratic flight. Launched properly, the model should fly a circle and then, if enough altitude remains, finish up in a straight line.

For a circle to the right, hold the model out at your right, nose pointed toward the left (Fig. 5–9a). Pull your hand straight across toward the left and release the model (b).

For a complete circle that returns to your hand, hold the model clear up on edge and launch it at high speed. I have had some models that would perform two complete circles and return to my hand. Such trick flights depend on precise balance and careful launching—both of which require considerable practice.

## Turns

A turn is simply an incomplete circle. So to make your model fly a turn hold it in position for a circle, but bank it less (Fig. 5–10) and don't push it so hard. The model should fly part of a turn, then straighten out into a normal straight-line glide.

If you find you do well with turns, you might try your hand at S-turns. For a left-right S-turn, give your model a little right rudder and then launch it in a left turn. The model should fly part of a left turn, slow down, level out and go into a right turn. For a right-left S-turn, simply reverse the procedure.

Fig. 5–10

Whatever you do, don't try to fly turns with a poorly aligned model that turns when launched for a straight glide. If it had a tendency to turn, say, to the left, when launched straight, it will lose altitude or dive on being launched to fly a left turn. When launched for a right turn, it will climb. On the other hand, if a model makes perfect turns in both directions, it is pretty sure to fly straight when so launched.

## Loops

Loops are made in a path perpendicular to the ground. To prepare your model for a loop, you must first, of course, get it to fly a straight glide. Your next step is to give the model extra up-elevator. Curl up the trailing edge of the tail (or the rearmost horizontal surface) somewhat more than for a normal glide.

Now, if the model has a keel, grasp it between thumb and index finger. Aim the nose downward somewhat more than for a normal glide. Then quickly hurl the airplane straight ahead like a spear. Launching speed should be considerably faster than for a normal glide. Also, the straight launching path is vital. Any twist of the wrist or curving swing of the arm at the time of release will send the airplane into an undesirable path. Properly launched, the model should perform a standard loop.

If the airplane is a Barnaby, or other model without a keel, grasp it by the leading edge and launch it fairly fast on a slightly downward path, as indicated in Fig. 5–11. If the model does not fly all the way around a loop, try a faster launch or more up-elevator, or perhaps a little of both. Be sure the wings are level at launch. If the model is tilted sideways, it will do a climbing turn and dive instead of a loop.

Fig. 5–11

After completing a loop, a model will probably do a series of roller-coaster dives and climbs. If properly balanced, they should gradually dampen out into normal glide—possibly with slight up-and-down undulations because of the stabilizing effect of the increased elevator.

There is another way to loop the loop. Hold the model nose-up with the top surface away from you. Now pull the airplane straight up, releasing the model in front of your face. The airplane should loop away from you, then return so you can catch it in your hand.

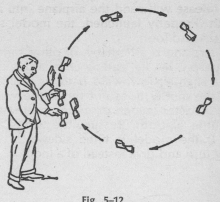

Fig. 5–12

# 6

# Competitions and Airshows

The fun has just begun. Now that you know how to make and fly paper airplanes, it's time to spread your wings a little. Flying paper models by yourself is endlessly fascinating, it's true. But like sailboating or soaring, flying models is much more fun in company—and even more so in competition with others.

Alone you get a false impression of your ability. In company you are put on your mettle. You must prove your flying skills and the soundness of your model's design.

So why not get your friends together and organize a paper airplane contest? There are many ways in which you can rate paper airplane performance. Distance flown, time in flight, maneuverability, best in show are some main events. You will probably think up other classes of competition.

You can run a formal contest in your school gymnasium or improvise a home event on a rainy weekend. Generally, it's best to hold paper airplane contests indoors. There the models will not be buffeted about by the air currents that are almost always present outdoors. From time to time, of course, especially in the evening hours, the wind may die down into a calm in which models may be flown. But you can't count on a calm when scheduling a paper airplane meet.

## Distance

The simplest class of competition is distance flown from a normal hand launching. Generally, paper models have a glide ratio of between 5-to-1 and 10-to-1. In practice, this means that a model launched from an altitude of five feet will glide between 25 and 50 feet. A flight of more than 50 feet would be extremely unusual.

You will need a tape to measure performance. Also, you will find measuring easier if you lay out markers indicating, say, five-foot intervals from the release point.

All launchings should be made in still air, from the same spot, at the same height above level ground. If the ground is not level, you'll find it difficult to judge performance, for flights that end at different heights below the release point will not be comparable.

When planning distance contests, you will want to consider the following questions. Who should launch the entries? Should one person—say, a nonparticipant such as one of the judges—make all the launchings? This would solve the problem of height of release. But it raises a further question. Can anyone other than the builder satisfactorily launch his model?

What about launching speed? Should a contestant be allowed to launch his model at any speed he chooses? Or must he launch it at its normal gliding speed, so that its path will be one continuous sloping glide?

A good solution is to admit all such categories as separate events: launch by the builder at normal speed, launch by the builder at slow and fast speeds. Then, in a free-for-all, each contestant may choose both style and speed of launch, and fly his model himself.

## Duration

In duration contests, the important thing is time in flight—that is, time elapsed from release to touchdown. These times are rather short—ten seconds would be a long flight—so for accurate comparisons you will need a stopwatch that measures to the nearest tenth of a second.

Since only time aloft counts, it is not absolutely necessary for a model to fly in a straight line, as in a distance event. Just the same, for good time performance, straight flight is preferable for this reason: when a model flies in as straight a line as possible its drag is at a minimum. So its sinking speed is also at a minimum and its time in flight is at a maximum.

## Special Events

Since many model builders also pride themselves on their launching skill, you might want to run special distance and duration events in which contestants adjust and launch one another's models.

The results may give some interesting answers to the

question "Is good performance the result of the launcher's skill or the designer's?"

## Maneuverability

In maneuverability contests, each contestant puts his model through aerial stunts that he names in advance. Circles, double circles, S-turns and loops are the usual events. These contests present the greatest challenge to a person's skill. The slightest defect in adjustment or launch will send a model way off course.

## Aerial Golf

An unusual competition that makes use of maneuvers is one I call "aerial golf." A course is laid out over some large distance and the object of the game is to fly the course in the smallest number of flights. Each launching after the first one is made from the spot where the model touched down on its previous flight.

Indoors, an aerial golf course might start at your front door and then proceed through halls and rooms, up and down stairs, returning finally to the starting point or ending at a back door—depending, of course, on the arrangement of your home. Outdoors, an obvious course would be around a building.

## A Final Word

Because of their lightness, paper model airplanes will take a lot of banging against walls, furniture and other obstacles, with little injury to themselves or what they strike. The chief hazard to the model and its delicate adjustments is inept handling—usually by enthusiastic onlookers who in picking up a model to return it to you will inadvertently twist it out of shape.

This is something you will just have to learn to put up with. At worst, you can always go back to the drawing board and make a new and better aircraft.

Of course, at competitions you may not have the

time to replace craft knocked out of commission by spectators. There the best policy is to permit only judges and other officials to retrieve the models.

But you may require some pretty agile officials. For, as you have probably noticed by now, paper airplanes have a habit of alighting in out-of-the-way, if not impossible-to-reach, places. Indeed, the consistent performance of all models in that respect has led to formal statement of the phenomenon. A colleague of mine has dubbed it *Barnaby's law:*

*Regardless of direction or technique of launch, a paper airplane will invariably come to rest at the most inaccessible landing site.*

In parting, I can only wish that you may get as much pleasure—and education—out of paper model airplanes as I have.

R.S. Barnaby 1967

# Glossary

AERODYNAMICS—The study of the motion of the air and its physical effects on bodies moving through it.

AILERON—In an airplane, a hinged horizontal control surface at the trailing edge of a wing, which controls rolling. In a paper model, the outer portions of the trailing edge of the wings, which are bent up or down to control rolling.

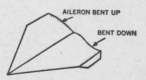

AIRCRAFT—Any air-supported vehicle.

AIRFOIL SECTION—A vertical fore-and-aft cross-section of an airfoil showing its characteristic curvature.

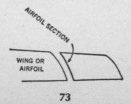

AIRPLANE—A fixed-wing, engine-driven aircraft supported by the lift of its wings, which results from its motion through the air.

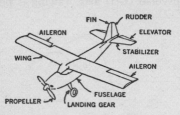

AIR RESISTANCE—*See* Drag.

AIRSPEED—The speed or velocity at which a body moves through the air or the air passes a body immersed in it; measured in miles per hour or in feet per second.

ALTITUDE—Height of a craft above a given reference surface; usually measured in feet. (In this book, altitude refers to the paper airplane's height above the ground on which the launcher is standing.)

ANGLE—*See* Attack, Angle of; Dihedral Angle; Glide Angle.

ATMOSPHERE—The blanket of air surrounding the earth; the air in which we live and fly.

ATTACK, ANGLE OF—The angle the chord of the wing makes with its flight path through the air; measured in degrees.

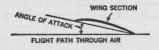

ATTITUDE—The position of a body with respect to its surroundings or to its flight path; e.g., right side up, upside down, nose up, nose down, level, banked, etc.

AXES OF ROTATION (*singular:* AXIS)—Three imaginary lines that pass through an aircraft's center of gravity at right angles to each other.

An aircraft changes its attitude in flight by rolling sideways, pitching (turning nose up or down), or turning from side to side—or combinations thereof. Rolling is performed about the fore-and-aft (X–X) axis. Pitching is performed about the transverse (Y–Y) axis. Yawing is performed about the vertical (Z–Z) axis.

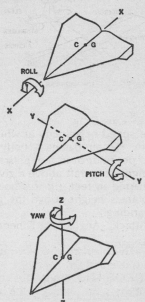

BALLAST—Weight used for adjusting balance.

BANK—To tip sideways, rotating about the fore-and-aft (X–X) axis. Used in turns to prevent skidding.

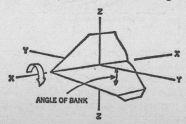

BAROMETER—An instrument that measures atmospheric pressure, usually in terms of the height in inches of a column of mercury.

The normal atmospheric pressure at sea level is about equivalent to a 30-inch column of mercury.

CAMBER—The characteristic curve of a wing or airfoil surface. *See* Airfoil Section.

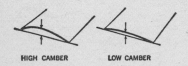

HIGH CAMBER       LOW CAMBER

CANARD (French for "wild duck")—A type of aircraft in which the horizontal stabilizer and elevators are located in front of the main wings.

CENTER OF GRAVITY (abbreviated CG)—The point at which a model, if hung by a thread, would balance in normal flying attitude.

CENTER OF LIFT (abbreviated CL)—The point at which, if a model's lift were concentrated there, the effect on the model would be the same as the effect of the actual distribution of lift.

CHORD—An imaginary line connecting the leading edge and trailing edge of a wing along the fore-and-aft direction. The angle this line makes with the flight path is the angle of attack.

← CHORD →

CONTROL SURFACES—*See* Aileron, Elevator, Elevon, Rudder.

DIHEDRAL ANGLE—The angle the wings make with the lateral (X–X) axis when the model is viewed from dead ahead.

If the wings are tipped downward, the angle is called *cathedral angle.*

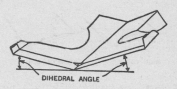

DIHEDRAL ANGLE

DIRECTIONAL STABILITY—Stability about the vertical (Z–Z) axis. The ability to return to straight flight after being disturbed by a yawing force. *See* Yaw.

DRAG—The force or resistance exerted by the air on a body moving through it. Drag is exerted in a direction opposite to the direction of motion.

ELEVATOR—A hinged horizontal control surface located behind (or in the case of a canard, ahead of) the center of gravity, which controls pitch.

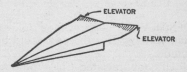

ELEVATOR
ELEVATOR

ELEVON—A hinged horizontal control surface that acts both as elevator and aileron. When two elevons are turned up or down the same amount, they act as elevators. When one is turned more than the other, they act as ailerons, imparting a rolling force to the model.

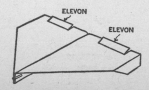

ELEVON
ELEVON

FIN—A vertical fore-and-aft surface extending above the other parts of the model, which provides directional stability. *See* Keel.

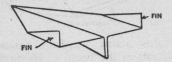

GLIDE—To coast downhill on the air, propelled by the force of gravity, like a sled or toboggan on a hill.

GLIDE ANGLE—The slope of a glider's flight path. Usually given as the ratio of horizontal distance covered per unit of altitude lost; e.g., 10 to 1. In a glider, the ratio of lift to drag.

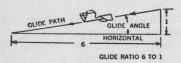

GLIDER—A heavier-than-air winged aircraft having no power plant, which maintains flight speed by gliding.

KEEL—A vertical fore-and-aft surface along the bottom of an aircraft, which increases directional stability and lateral stability.

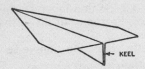

LATERAL STABILITY—Stability about the fore-and-aft (X–X) axis of a model.

The ability to return to a laterally level attitude after being disturbed by a rolling force. *See* Roll.

LEADING EDGE—The forward edge of a surface or wing as it moves through the air.

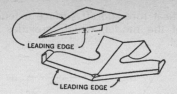

LIFT—The force acting vertically upward against the wings of an aircraft as the result of its motion through the air. The force of lift opposes the force of gravity.

LONGITUDINAL STABILITY—Stability about the transverse (Y–Y) axis.

The ability to return to normal gliding flight after being made to dive or nose upward by some external force. *See* Pitch.

MANEUVER—(*verb*) To perform a desired flight path or pattern. (*noun*) A desired flight path or pattern; e.g., a loop or a circle.

MANEUVERABLE—Having the ability to be steered through desired flight paths or patterns.

NEGATIVE ANGLE OF ATTACK—A wing position in which the leading edge is lower than the trailing edge so that when the wing moves through the air a downward force is exerted on it.

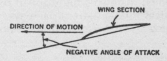

NOSE HEAVY—A condition in which the center of gravity is located ahead of the center of lift so that a craft tends to dive.

PITCH—To rotate about the transverse (Y–Y) axis; to tip up or down.

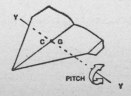

PLANFORM—The outline of a model as viewed from directly above.

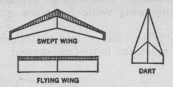

POSITIVE ANGLE OF ATTACK—A wing position in which the leading edge is higher than the trailing edge so that when the wing moves through the air an upward force is exerted on it.

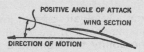

ROLL—To rotate about the fore-and-aft (X–X) axis; to rock sideways.

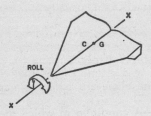

ROTATE—To turn about an axis.
RUDDER—An adjustable vertical surface at the rear of an aircraft, which controls yawing.

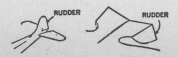

SIDESLIP—(*verb*) To slide sideways toward the center of a turn because of too much bank.

(*noun*) A sidewise motion of an airplane caused by the lowering of one wing while the plane is proceeding in a straight line.

SINKING SPEED—Rate of loss of altitude during gliding flight, usually measured in feet per second.

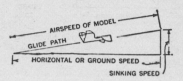

SKID—To slide sideways away from the center of a turn because of insufficient bank.

SOAR—To glide in an air current rising as fast as or faster than the sinking speed of the glider.

STABILITY—The ability to return to a normal flight path after being deflected therefrom.

STABLE—Having the ability to return to a normal flight path after being deflected from it.

STALL—(*verb*) To slow down to an airspeed insufficient to maintain normal flight, usually as a result of a climb or nose-up attitude.

(*noun*) Abrupt loss of lift caused by placing the wing at an angle of attack greater than the angle of greatest lift.

SYMMETRICAL—A paper airplane is symmetrical when the size, shape, and setting of the parts on one side of its vertical centerline plane are a mirror image of the parts on the other side.

TAIL HEAVY—A condition in which the center of gravity is located behind the center of lift, so that a craft tends to nose-up and stall.

TAIL SURFACES—The stabilizing and control surfaces at the rear of a model.

TENDER—Easily disturbed from a normal flight path.
TRAILING EDGE—The rear edge of a surface or wing.

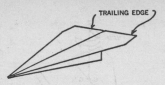

TRAJECTORY—The curving path followed by a body without wings or lifting surfaces when launched into the air and acted upon only by the launching force, the resistance of the air, and the force of gravity.

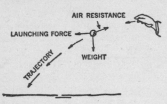

TRANSVERSE—Lateral, crosswise.
TURBULENCE—Rough and irregular flow of air around and behind an obstacle that has disturbed its smooth flow. Turbulence may also be caused by up-currents due to local heating of the air.
UNDULATION—A wavy up-and-down or roller-coaster-like motion.
VELOCITY—*See* Airspeed.
VERTICAL SURFACES—*See* Fin, Keel, Rudder.
WAKE—The turbulence behind a body immersed in and moving through the air.
WING—The supporting surface of an airplane or glider.
WING CURVE—*See* Camber.
WINGSPAN—The distance from wingtip to wingtip.

YAW—To rotate about the vertical (Z–Z) axis; to turn to the right or left.

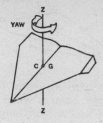

# Bantam Book Catalog

It lists over a thousand money-saving best-sellers originally priced from $3.75 to $15.00 —bestsellers that are yours now for as little as 50¢ to $2.95!

The catalog gives you a great opportunity to build your own private library at huge savings!

So don't delay any longer—send us your name and address and 25¢ (to help defray postage and handling costs).